All this CLAW-SOME fun inside...

JURASSIC EXPLORERS

PRESENTS

THE WORLD OF DINOSAURS

THIS BOOK BELONGS TO

Edson

Write your name here.

Turn the page to begin your dinosaur adventure…

LB BOOKS

Published 2023. Little Brother Books Ltd, Ground Floor, 23 Southernhay East, Exeter, Devon EX1 1QL
books@littlebrotherbooks.co.uk | www.littlebrotherbooks.co.uk
Printed in China. EU address: Korte Leemstraat 3, 2018 Antwerpen, Belgium

WHAT IS A DINOSAUR?

Some were big some were small, some had scales and some had feathers, but all dinosaurs had these things in common.

1 THEY HATCHED FROM AN EGG

Every single dinosaur, whatever size they grew up to be, began life in an egg. The biggest eggs were the size of two flattened footballs and the smallest were less than 2.5cm.

2 THEY WERE REPTILES

All dinosaurs belonged to a group of animals known as reptiles. Other reptiles, like pterosaurs and plesiosaurs, lived at the same time but they weren't dinosaurs.

3 THEY HAD CLAWS

The number and size varied but every dinosaur had claws. They had many uses including fighting, killing prey and gathering food.

4 THEY HAD FOUR LIMBS

Although many dinosaurs walked on two legs, they all had four limbs. Some had longer hind legs and shorter forearms, whereas others had similar-sized front and back legs.

5 THEY HAD A TAIL

Some were long and some were short, some had feathers and some had spikes but every dinosaur had a tail of some kind. They helped dinosaurs keep balance when moving quickly and some were used as weapons or to attract a mate.

6 THEY WALKED ON UPRIGHT LEGS

Dinosaurs walked on their toes with their legs held directly under their bodies, unlike their lizard and crocodilian relatives.

MAKE A MATCH

Can you match these dinosaurs into pairs? Which one doesn't have a match?

A
B
C
D
E
F
G

Answers on pages 76-77

FINISH

MEET THE
PREDATORS

No animal was safe when these ferocious hunters were around!

Strong neck for tossing prey in the air.

WOW!

Fearsome Tyrannosaurus had the strongest bite of any land animal that's ever lived.

IT'S A FACT!

Tyrannosaurus only lived for about 30 years.

Strong legs for running up to 12 mph.

TYRANNOSAURUS

DINO REPORT

NAME: Tyrannosaurus
(tye-RAN-oh-SORE-us)

MEANING:
Tyrant lizard

SIZE: 12m

FOOD: Meat

60 sharp teeth,
the size of
large bananas.

DID YOU KNOW?

Gigantic Tyrannosaurus
weighed as much as
three hippos.

Short arms may
have been used
to hold prey.

FOOD FACT

Copy the letters into the matching coloured
circles to reveal where Tyrannosaurus came
on the Cretaceous food chain.

P T O ○ ○ ○

Answers on pages 76-77

VELOCIRAPTOR

DINO REPORT

NAME: Velociraptor
(veh-loss-ih-RAP-tore)

MEANING:
Speed thief

SIZE: 2m

FOOD: Meat

Feathered body.

IT'S A FACT!

Speedy Velociraptor could run up to 25 mph.

DID YOU KNOW?

Small Velociraptor was only as big as a wolf.

WOW!
Velociraptor was probably nocturnal. Its sharp sense of smell would have helped when hunting in the dark.

Long, stiff tail for balance.

Muscly legs for fast running.

Sharp claws to pin down prey.

TRUE OR FALSE?
Velociraptor was covered in scales.

Circle the correct answer.

TRUE   FALSE

ALLOSAURUS

DINO REPORT

NAME: Allosaurus (Al-oh-saw-russ)

MEANING: Other lizard

SIZE: 12m

FOOD: Meat

Unusual bony ridges.

Knife-like teeth that were replaced when they fell out.

DID YOU KNOW?

Allosaurus preferred to hunt alone. Fossils show that those in packs often attacked each other.

WOW!

Allosaurus had teeth which curved backwards to stop prey escaping.

Sharp claws for tearing prey apart.

UP CLOSE

Which close-up isn't of Allosaurus?

 **A**

 **B**

 **C**

COELOPHYSIS

DINO REPORT

NAME: Coelophysis
(seel-OH-fie-sis)

MEANING:
Hollow form

SIZE: 3m

FOOD: Meat

Long, narrow snout with blade-like teeth.

Long neck that could turn quickly when hunting prey.

Grasping claws for catching reptiles.

DID YOU KNOW?

Coelophysis had good eyesight which helped it spot and track its small prey.

WOW!

Coelophysis had hollow bones so it was light and could run fast.

EGG COUNT

How many Coelophysis eggs can you count in this jumble?

Answers on pages 76-77

DINO WORDS

COLOURING FUN

What colours will you choose for this plant-eating Stegosaurus?

ON THE RUN

Can you spot eight dino differences between these two Allosaurus pictures?

Colour a meteor each time you spot a difference.

1 2 3 4

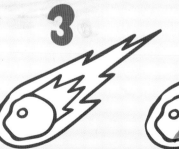

Answers on pages 76-77

DINOSAUR A-Z

There's one for every letter of the alphabet!

Discover lots of roar-some facts in this dino A to Z.

A
APATOSAURUS

This bulky beast had a strong neck which it may have used to fight other dinos.

B
BONES

A lot of what we know about dinosaurs comes from the bones which have been discovered all over the world.

C
CLAWS

All dinosaurs had claws – some were super sharp. They were used for lots of things including gathering food, fighting and slashing prey.

D
DUCK-BILLED

Duck-billed dinosaurs, such as Parasaurolophus and Maiasaura, had wide, flat mouths that looked similar to a duck's beak. Inside they had up to 1000 teeth to grind up their food.

E EGG

All dinosaurs hatched from an egg, even the ones that grew up to be enormous!

F FOSSIL

Dinosaur fossils are the remains of dinosaurs that died a long time ago that have been preserved in the Earth. Before dinosaur fossils were discovered, people had no idea that these incredible creatures had ever existed.

G GIGANOTOSAURUS

This dino giant was one of the largest predators to ever walk the Earth. It weighed as much as 125 people.

H HABITAT

Dinosaurs lived in many different habitats including deserts, woodlands and coastlines.

I IGUANODON

This herbivore had an unusual thumb spike on its hand which was used to fend off attackers.

J JURASSIC

Dinosaurs such as Allosaurus and Stegosaurus lived in the Jurassic period which was 200-145 million years ago.

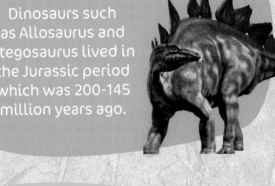

K KILL

Most meat-eating dinosaurs used their sharp teeth and deadly claws to kill their prey.

L LIZARD

The word dinosaur means 'terrible lizard'. Dinosaurs were reptiles, just like the lizards that are alive today.

MAPUSAURUS

This fierce carnivore had dagger-like teeth. Even a baby Mapusaurus could tear meat from a dead dinosaur.

NEST

Dinosaurs such as Maiasaurus and Oviraptor built nests to keep their eggs warm and safe. Some dinosaurs sat on their eggs, like hens do today, while others covered them with plants.

OMNIVORE

Most dinosaurs ate either meat or plants but some, including Eoraptor, were omnivores that ate both.

PREDATOR

Most meat-eating dinosaurs were predators which meant they hunted other animals for food.

QUARRY

In 1909, a quarry containing hundreds of tonnes of dinosaur bones was discovered in Utah, USA. Today the site is home to the Dinosaur National Monument where visitors can see more than 1,500 dinosaur fossils still contained in the quarry wall.

RIOJASAURUS

This slow-moving dino had thick legs like an elephant. It probably lived in herds to help protect against predators.

SPIKES

Some dinosaurs, including Euoplocephalus and Stegosaurus, had spikes on their back or on the end of their tail. These would have been used like armour for protection or as a weapon to fend off attackers.

TYRANNOSAURUS

Known as the dinosaur king, Tyrannosaurus is probably the world's most famous dino. This ferocious giant lived in Canada and the USA 68-66 million years ago.

UTAHRAPTOR

This feathered predator had huge toe claws which it used to slash its prey.

VERTEBRATE

All dinosaurs were vertebrates which means they had an internal skeleton and backbone.

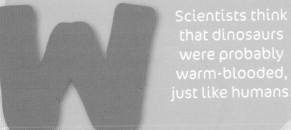

WARM-BLOODED

Scientists think that dinosaurs were probably warm-blooded, just like humans.

EXTINCT

Dinosaurs became extinct 66 million years ago when a meteorite struck Earth and caused the climate to change.

YANGCHUANOSAURUS

At 11m long, this terrifying meat-eater may have been the biggest predator in Asia during the Jurassic period.

ZIGONG DINOSAUR MUSEUM

This museum in China claims to have the largest number of dinosaur fossils in the world. It is built around a quarry where skeletons of perfectly preserved Shunosaurus were discovered.

ON THE MOVE

Use a pencil to follow the trails these roaming dinosaurs have left behind.

STOMP!

STOMP!

TOOT!

TOOT!

ZOOM!

ZOOM!

Draw a trail for the mighty Tyrannosaurus.

Nice and slow! Follow the Stegosaurus!

Follow that sound! It's the musical Parasaurolophus!

Quick as a flash! Catch the speedy Coelophysis!

DINO MATCH

Can you draw lines to match these body parts together to make two complete dinosaurs?

Each dinosaur needs a head, a body, a tail, arms and legs.

Answers on pages 76-77

MEET THE ONES WITH WEAPONS

These tough dinos knew how to defend themselves with their powerful built-in weapons.

1m long horns over each eye.

Large frill protected the neck like a shield.

Hundreds of teeth to grind down plants.

WOW!
Rival Triceratops fought over food by locking their horns together.

IT'S A FACT!
Triceratops used its three horns as weapons, charging headfirst at predators who tried to attack.

TRICERATOPS

DID YOU KNOW?

Ginormous Triceratops had one of the biggest skulls of any land animal.

DINO REPORT

NAME: Triceratops (tri-SERRA-tops)

MEANING: Three-horned face

SIZE: 9m

FOOD: Plants

Bulky body which made it hard to run fast.

SHADOW FUN

Which shadow matches this picture of Triceratops exactly?

A   B   C

Answers on pages 76-77

STEGOSAURUS

DINO REPORT

NAME: Stegosaurus
(STEG-oh-SORE-us)

MEANING:
Roof lizard

SIZE: 9m

FOOD: Plants

Back plates
for attracting
a mate.

WOW!

Although Stegosaurus
was as long as a bus,
its brain was only the
size of a plum.

Strong legs
to support its
heavy weight.

DID YOU KNOW?

Every plate on a Stegosaurus's back was different.

IT'S A FACT!

Plant-eating Stegosaurus didn't have any teeth. Instead, it used its sharp beak to nibble plants.

Enormous body as big as an elephant's.

Sharp tail spikes that were used as a weapon.

STOMPING STEGOSAURUS

How many Stegosaurus footprints can you count on these pages?

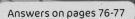

Answers on pages 76-77

ANKYLOSAURUS

DINO REPORT

NAME: Ankylosaurus
(an-KIE-loh-sore-us)

MEANING:
Stiff lizard

SIZE: 10m

FOOD: Plants

Bony tail club for attacking.

WOW!

Ankylosaurus's tail club was big enough for a human to sit on and strong enough to break bone.

Bulky body that was wider than it was tall.

DID YOU KNOW?

Ankylosaurus was covered in thick plates, spikes and studs which acted like armour to protect the dino from predators.

Beak-like mouth for stripping and snipping plants.

QUESTION TIME

What did Ankylosaurus use its tail club for? Circle the right answer.

balancing   attacking

PACHYCEPHALOSAURUS

Large skull shaped like a dome.

WOW!

Pachycephalosaurus may have used its hard head to head-butt other dinosaurs that dared to get close.

Eyes set forward in the skull for good 3D vision.

DINO REPORT

NAME:
Pachycephalosaurus
(pack-i-KEF-al-oh-sore-russ)

MEANING:
Thick headed lizard

SIZE: 8m

FOOD: Plants

DID YOU KNOW?

A Pachycephalosaurus skull was 20 times thicker than other dinosaur skulls.

Walked on two legs.

DIFFERENT DINO

Which Pachycephalosaurus is the odd one out?

Ⓐ   Ⓑ   Ⓒ

Answers on pages 76-77

DRAW T-REX

Follow the instructions below to draw your very own claw-some Tyrannosaurus.

YOU WILL NEED

Sheet of white A4 paper

Pencil

Rubber

Coloured Pens

HOW TO DRAW

1

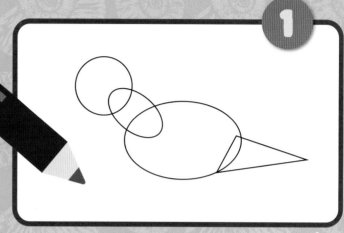

Draw an oval shape for the body then add an oval neck, round head and triangular tail.

2

Rub out the unneeded lines around the neck and tail. Draw two oval shapes for the arm and an oval and circle for the leg.

3

Rub out the unneeded lines on the leg. Add a second leg and two oval-shaped feet.

4

Rub out the unneeded lines on the arm and legs, then draw a square shape with rounded corners on the end of the face.

5

Draw a triangle shape on the square to create an open mouth, then rub out the unneeded lines. Draw small ovals on the feet and hands.

6

Add an eye and a nostril, then rub out the unneeded lines on the arm and leg.

7

Rub out the unneeded lines on the body and add triangle shapes along the neck, back and tail. Draw claws on each hand and foot, then rub out the unneeded lines.

8

Colour your Tyrannosaurus in to bring it to life.

DINO DATES

Dinosaurs ruled the world for millions of years. Let's find out more about the time periods they lived in.

COELOPHYSIS

PLATEOSAURUS

DIPLODOCUS

JURASSIC PERIOD
(200-145 million years ago)

The climate became cooler and wetter during the **Jurassic Period**. Lots of new plants and forests grew so there was plenty of food for herbivores to eat. Many new dinosaurs appeared and some grew to be huge.

TRICERATOPS

TYRANNOSAURUS

DID YOU KNOW?

Dinosaurs lived in the Mesozoic Era which was divided into three periods – Triassic, Jurassic and Cretaceous.

HERRERASAURUS

TRIASSIC PERIOD
(251-200 million years ago)

The **Triassic Period** saw the very first dinosaurs. Back then, the world was hot and dry and the land was desert-like. Early dinosaurs were small compared to the giants that came later.

ALLOSAURUS

STEGOSAURUS

SPINOSAURUS

CRETACEOUS PERIOD
(145-66 million years ago)

During the **Cretaceous Period** dinosaurs lived all over the world. Many developed horns and armour. The period ended when an asteroid crashed into Earth causing dinosaurs to become extinct.

WHO IS IT?

Read the clues below and see if you can work out which dinosaur is being described.

I walked on two legs.

I was **big**.

I had an eye-catching sail.

I had a snout like a crocodile's.

I was a meat-eater.

Circle the dinosaur that's being described.

OVIRAPTOR

SPINOSAURUS

TRICERATOPS

TYRANNOSAURUS

Answers on pages 76-77

WORD HUNT

Can you find all of these dinosaur words hidden in the wordsearch below?

H	O	R	N	A	L	D	E	O	F
B	S	C	V	W	K	I	X	L	O
A	F	E	M	F	T	U	P	E	S
G	H	Q	B	Z	A	T	O	U	S
D	T	H	F	L	I	S	R	B	I
N	E	K	S	G	L	E	T	W	L
Y	E	O	G	J	S	U	A	R	N
C	T	V	D	J	V	E	G	G	E
G	H	T	S	F	C	T	Q	I	D
A	O	P	C	L	A	W	S	F	W

Colour a footprint as you find each word.

FOSSIL   HORN   EGG   CLAWS   TAIL   TEETH

1   2   3   4   5   6

DINO SUPERSTARS!

Let's meet the dinosaurs who smashed the records...

★★★★★

BIGGEST PREDATOR

At 16m, or as long as three cars, the deadly Spinosaurus was the biggest meat-eating dino.

★★★★★

MOST TEETH

Lambeosaurus and other hadrosaurs had more than 1,000 teeth. Lambeosaurus's teeth fell out and regrew throughout its life.

★★★★★

LONGEST CLAWS

At 1m in length, Therizinosaurus not only had the longest claws of any dinosaur, it also had the longest claws of any animal in history.

★★★★★

FIRST BELLY BUTTON

A fossil of plant-eating Psittacosaurus was the first to show that some dinosaurs had belly buttons.

★★★★★

LONGEST

Diplodocus could grow to over 50m from the tip of its tail to the end of its mouth. That's as long as two swimming pools.

★★★★★

SMALLEST BRAIN

When comparing body size to brain size, Stegosaurus is the winner. At 9m long, its small brain was only the size of an apple.

★★★★★

STRONGEST BITE

The award for strongest bite force goes to the ferocious Tyrannosaurus. Its mighty bite was three times as powerful as a lion's and could crush bone.

COLOUR THE STARS TO GIVE EACH RECORD-BREAKING DINO A RATING.

HEAVIEST

It's estimated that hefty Argentinosaurus weighed as much as 20 elephants.

★★★★★

TALLEST

With its long legs and neck, Sauroposeidon could grow as tall as 18m – the height of a six storey building.

FASTEST

Reaching speeds of up to 50mph, super quick Gallimimus could run faster than a racehorse.

PREHISTORIC PUZZLE

Journey back in time to answer the questions about this prehistoric picture.

1 How many bones can you count?

2 Can you find this fossil?

3 How many dinosaur footprints are there?

A

Answers on pages 76-77

DINO DESIGN

Use this space to create your very own dinosaur. You get to decide how it looks, what it eats and how scary it is!

DINOSAUR REPORT

My dinosaur is called _____osaurus

It is _____ million years old

It is the size of a _____

It weighs as much as _____

It eats _____

FEATURES:

Sharp teeth

Long neck

Back plates

Horns

Tail spike

SKILLS

Speed

Strength

Fierce roar

Powerful bite

Sharp eyesight

Draw your dino here.

How long are your dinosaur's claws?

Does your dinosaur walk on two legs or four?

Is your dinosaur fierce or friendly?

45

MEET THE GIANTS

These super-sized dinosaurs were some of the largest creatures to ever roam the Earth.

WOW!

When Diplodocus swished its tail, it made a loud noise like a cannon being fired.

DID YOU KNOW?

Plant-eating Diplodocus swallowed stones to help digest the food inside its stomach.

Long tail that could be used like a whip.

Thick, column-like legs for supporting the heavy body.

DIPLODOCUS

DINO REPORT

NAME: Diplodocus
(DIP-low DOCK-us)

MEANING:
Double beam

SIZE: 27m

FOOD: Plants

Peg-like teeth for stripping leaves from branches.

Long neck that could be lifted to eat from trees.

IT'S A FACT!

Heavy Diplodocus weighed as much as two African elephants.

DINO BONES

Draw lines from the words to the body parts to correctly label this Diplodocus skeleton.

Tail

Front legs

Back legs

Neck

Answers on pages 76-77

WOW!

Spinosaurus's sail was probably boldly coloured and may have been used to attract a mate.

IT'S A FACT!

Fish-eating Spinosaurus had high-up nostrils to help it breathe in water.

Enormous, bony sail.

DINO REPORT

NAME: Spinosaurus
(SPINE-oh-SORE-us)

MEANING:
Thorn lizard

SIZE: 16m

FOOD: Meat and fish

Webbed feet for walking in water.

SPINOSAURUS

Long, narrow snout like a crocodile's.

Cone-shaped teeth for catching slippery fish.

SUPER SAIL

Circle the Spinosaurus with the biggest sail.

A B C

Answers on pages 76-77

GIGANOTOSAURUS

DINO REPORT

NAME: Giganotosaurus
(gig-an-OH-toe-SORE-us)

MEANING:
Giant southern lizard

SIZE: 12m

FOOD: Meat

Muscly neck for lifting and holding heavy prey.

Blade-like teeth, perfect for slicing flesh.

WOW!

Some experts believe gigantic Giganotosaurus was even bigger and heavier than Tyrannosaurus.

Powerful hind legs for walking quickly.

DID YOU KNOW?

For such a big dinosaur, Giganotosaurus had a small brain – it was only about the size of a cucumber.

HOME SWEET HOME

Trace over the word to discover where Giganotosaurus lived.

Argentina

ARGENTINOSAURUS

DID YOU KNOW?
Argentinosaurus grew as tall as a two-storey house.

DINO REPORT
NAME: Argentinosaurus (AR-gent-eeno-sore-us)

MEANING: Argentina lizard

SIZE: 35m

FOOD: Plants

Air sacs in the neck bones helped reduce Argentinosaurus's weight.

Massive, heavy body.

4.5m long hind legs.

WOW!
An Argentinosaurus egg was about the size of a football. When first hatched, the baby dino was probably only about 1m long.

Circle the correct answer.

HOW BIG?
What was an Argentinosaurus egg the same size as?

Answers on pages 76-77

CODE CRACKER

Use the key to uncover these hidden facts about Suchomimus, the swamp-dwelling dino.

KEY

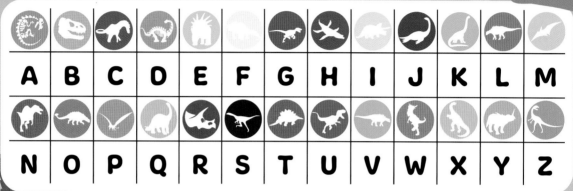

| A | B | C | D | E | F | G | H | I | J | K | L | M |
| N | O | P | Q | R | S | T | U | V | W | X | Y | Z |

1) Suchomimus had over 120

___ ___ ___ ___ ___

that curved backwards.

2) Suchomimus ate other dinosaurs and

___ ___ ___ ___

3) Suchomimus had

___ ___ ___ ___

like a crocodile's.

Answers on pages 76-77

DOTTY DINO

Join the dots to finish this picture of Triceratops, then add some roar-some colour.

SUPER SEQUENCE

Can you colour the white leaf the correct colour to complete the sequence?

PREHISTORIC RELATIVES

Did you know that some of the creatures who shared Earth with the dinosaurs are still around today?

THE HISTORY

Sixty-six million years ago, an asteroid hit Earth. It changed Earth's climate causing the dinosaurs to become extinct. Many other creatures were also wiped out but some managed to survive and are still living among us today.

CROCODILE COUSINS

The earliest relatives of the crocodile evolved around 200 million years ago, during the late Triassic and early Jurassic Periods, when dinosaurs roamed the Earth. These ancestors were smaller than today's crocs and had a shorter snout but they were just as fierce.

UNDERWATER WORLD

Prehistoric oceans were full of giant marine reptiles that don't exist today, but some creatures that lived during the time of the dinosaurs are still swimming in our seas. These include sharks, giant turtles and jellyfish.

FLYING DINOSAURS

Although the prehistoric skies were ruled by flying reptiles, birds appeared during the Jurassic Period. Fossils of one of the earliest known birds proved a link between dinosaurs and birds, which means the birds that fly in our skies today are related to the dinosaurs.

EARLY LIFE

Some of the insects on Earth today existed before the dinosaurs. Cockroaches, dragonflies and millipedes were here first and other insects like flies and bees appeared during the dinosaurs' reign.

DOTTY DISCOVERY

Join the dots to reveal another creature that lived alongside the dinosaurs.

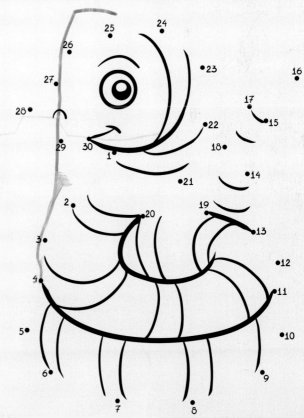

STOMPING FEET

Make and wear your very own dinosaur feet so you can stomp like a Tyrannosaurus.

YOU WILL NEED

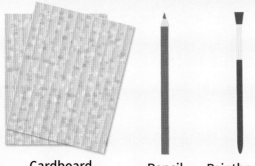

Cardboard   Pencil   Paintbrush

String

Scissors

Ruler

Green paint

Skewer

HOW TO MAKE

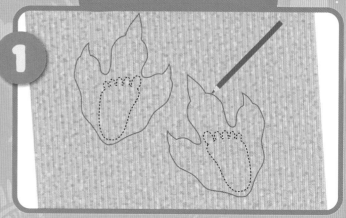

1

Draw two dinosaur feet on a piece of cardboard, bigger than your own feet.

2

Carefully cut out the dinosaur feet.

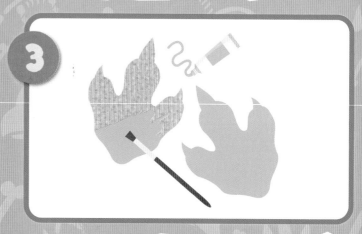

3

Paint both feet green and leave them to dry completely.

56

4

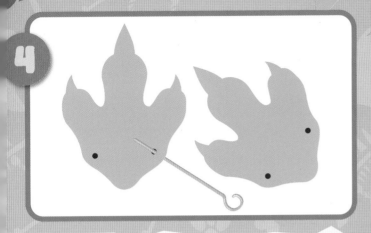

Use a skewer to carefully pierce a hole on either side of each foot, where shown in the picture above.

7

Stand on your dinosaur feet and tie the pieces of string into bows around your feet, as if you were tying a shoelace. Now you're ready to stomp like a dinosaur!

5

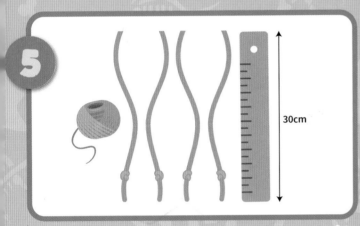

30cm

Cut four pieces of string, each about 30cm long, and tie a large knot in the end of each piece – the knots need to be bigger than the holes in the feet.

6

Thread the pieces of string through the holes so that the knots are on the underneath of the feet.

COUNT IT!
How many Tyrannosaurus footprints can you count in this trail?

MEGA MIX-UP

These dinosaurs have got themselves into a Jurassic jumble!

How many of each different dinosaur can you count?

Colour the meteor when you've finished.

ALLOSAURUS

DIPLODOCUS

STEGOSAURUS

DINO FAVES

What do you love most about dinosaurs?

Circle your favourite thing from each of the choices.

FIERCE	OR	FRIENDLY
GIGANTIC	OR	MINI
TYRANNOSAURUS	OR	SPINOSAURUS
HERBIVORE	OR	CARNIVORE
SHARP TEETH	OR	NO TEETH
STEGOSAURUS	OR	DIPLODOCUS
FEATHERS	OR	SCALES
LONG NECK	OR	LONG TAIL
ANKYLOSAURUS	OR	VELOCIRAPTOR
BACKPLATES	OR	SAIL
TAIL SPIKE	OR	CLAWS
APATOSAURUS	OR	ALLOSAURUS
TWO LEGS	OR	FOUR LEGS
HORNS	OR	CREST

RULING REPTILES

When dinosaurs ruled the land, the sky and sea were filled with other reptiles. Read on to meet some of them.

Tall head crest.

Enormous wings for flying, swooping and gliding.

Long, narrow beak for catching fish.

REPTILE REPORT

NAME: Pteranodon (tye-RAN-oh-don)

SIZE: 9m wingspan

FOOD: Fish

DID YOU KNOW?
Pteranodon only flapped its huge wings occasionally, the rest of the time it soared on the wind.

PTERANODON

Sharp teeth, each about the size of a banana.

DID YOU KNOW?
Gigantic Kronosaurus was nearly as long as two great white sharks.

REPTILE REPORT

NAME: Kronosaurus (crow-no-SORE-us)

SIZE: 10m

FOOD: Fish and marine reptiles

KRONOSAURUS

Strong flippers for powering through the water.

Crocodile-like jaws.

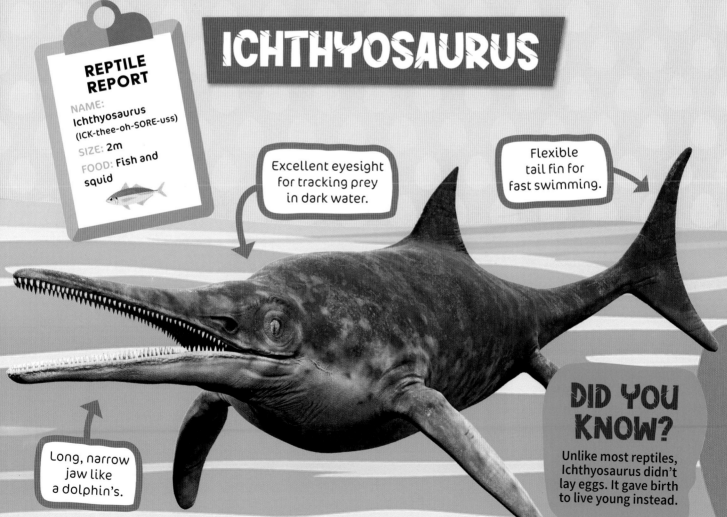

Long, narrow wings.

Diamond-shaped tail flap for steering.

RHAMPHORHYNCHUS

REPTILE REPORT
NAME:
Rhamphorhynchus (ram-foe-RINK-us)
SIZE:
1.5m wingspan
FOOD: Fish

Sharp, pointed teeth for catching fish.

ICHTHYOSAURUS

REPTILE REPORT
NAME:
Ichthyosaurus (ICK-thee-oh-SORE-uss)
SIZE: 2m
FOOD: Fish and squid

Excellent eyesight for tracking prey in dark water.

Flexible tail fin for fast swimming.

Long, narrow jaw like a dolphin's.

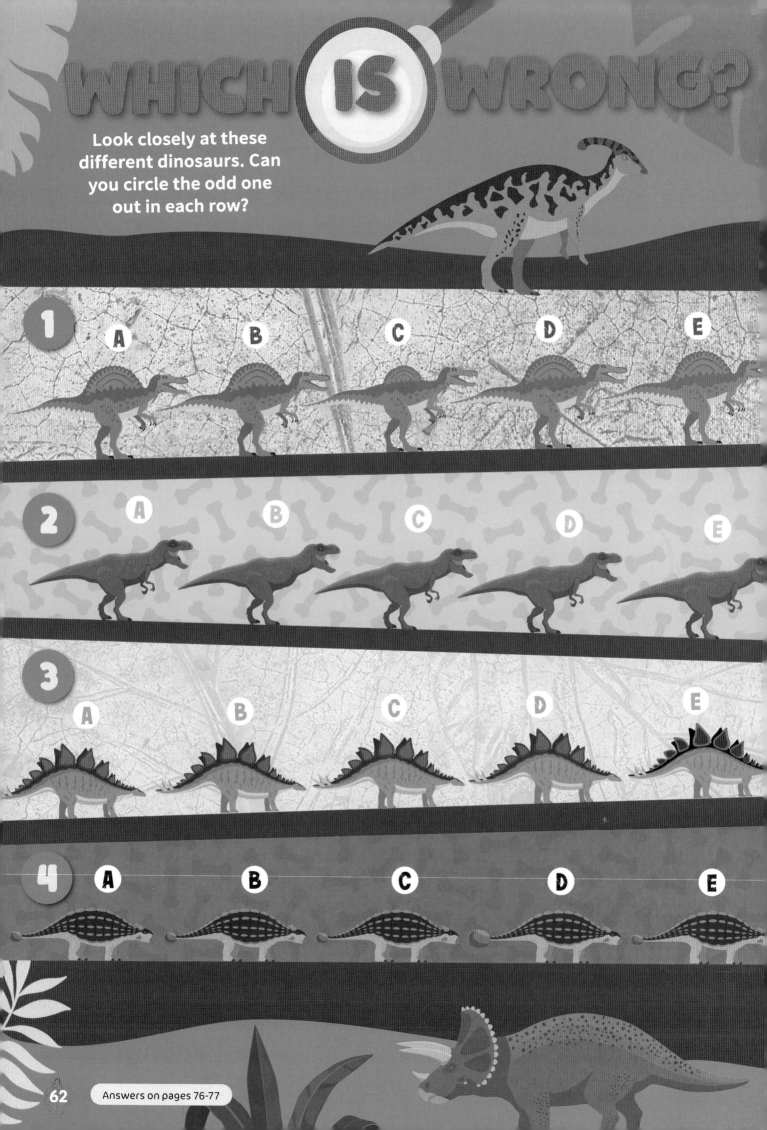

WHICH IS WRONG?

Look closely at these different dinosaurs. Can you circle the odd one out in each row?

1 A B C D E

2 A B C D E

3 A B C D E

4 A B C D E

Answers on pages 76-77

Like all animals, dinosaurs needed to poo. Scientists have discovered lots from studying their fossilised waste.

PREHISTORIC POO!

UP CLOSE
What a coprolite contains isn't always visible to the naked eye so scientists use very powerful magnifying glasses to take a closer look.

DID YOU KNOW?
A fossilised poo is called a coprolite.

HERBIVORE OR CARNIVORE?
Dinosaur coprolites are very useful as they can tell scientists what food a dinosaur ate. If fragments of bone are found, it shows the dinosaur was a carnivore. Herbivore poo might contain seeds, leaf remains or bark.

HIDDEN CLUES
As well as revealing what a dinosaur ate, a coprolite can also tell scientists about the types of plants that were growing in the dinosaur's habitat at that time.

BIG DISCOVERY
The biggest coprolite from a carnivore that has ever been found was discovered in the USA in 2019. At 75cm long and containing pieces of crushed bone, it is thought to belong to a Tyrannosaurus.

MEET THE
LITTLE ONES

WOW!

Microraptor's long, stiff tail may have helped keep it steady in the air.

DINO REPORT

NAME: Microraptor
(MIKE-row-rap-tor)

MEANING:
Small thief

SIZE: 1m

FOOD: Meat

Feathered tail for attracting mates.

MICRORAPTOR

64

IT'S A FACT!
Microraptor lived in China. More than 300 Microraptor fossils have been found which suggests it was a very common dinosaur.

DID YOU KNOW?
Microraptor couldn't fly but it was able to use its wings to glide.

Large eyes, possibly for hunting at night.

Bird-like beak lined with small sharp teeth.

Body covered in shiny black feathers.

COLOURING FUN
Add some colour to this mini Microraptor.

EORAPTOR

DINO REPORT

NAME: Eoraptor
(EE-oh-RAP-tor)

MEANING:
Dawn thief

SIZE: 1m

FOOD: Meat

WOW!

Eoraptor was the size of a large dog and probably weighed the same as a small child.

Long tail for keeping balance when running.

DID YOU KNOW?

Scientists don't know whether Eoraptor was covered in feathers or scales.

IT'S A FACT!

Eoraptor lived 251 million years ago and was one of the earliest dinosaurs.

Eyes that could see well in nearly all directions

Semi-hollow bones that reduced body weight.

Five fingers on each hand but only three had claws.

EGG HUNT

Can you spot this Eoraptor egg hidden somewhere on these pages?

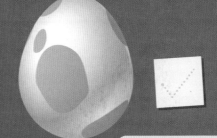

Answers on pages 76-77

CAUDIPTERYX

DINO REPORT

NAME: Caudipteryx
(caw-dip-ter-iks)

MEANING:
Tail feather

SIZE: 1m

FOOD: Meat and plants

Feathers for warmth.

WOW!
Small Caudipteryx was about the size of a turkey.

Short tail to wag when attracting mates.

DID YOU KNOW?
Fossils show that Caudipteryx had feathers of contrasting colours.

Long legs for running quickly.

ON THE RUN

Use a pen or pencil to trace the trial this speedy Caudipteryx has made.

COMPSOGNATHUS

DINO REPORT

NAME: Compsognathus
(komp-sag-NATH-us)

MEANING:
Pretty jaw

SIZE: 65cm

FOOD: Meat

Long neck that was mostly held horizontally.

DID YOU KNOW?

Everything scientists know about Compsognathus has come from just two fossils.

Long tail for balance when turning quickly.

Sharp claws for hunting.

WOW!

Tiny Compsognathus ran on tiptoes for super speed.

A   B   C

TINY DINO

Can you circle the smallest Compsognathus?

Answers on pages 76-77

COOL COLOURING

Add some dino-mite colours to bring this roaring T-rex to life!

DINO DOOR HANGER

Cut out and make this cool door hanger to let everyone know whether to come in or keep out!

HOW TO MAKE

1

Use scissors to carefully cut the door hanger out along the dotted lines.

2

Choose which side you want to show.

3

Hang the door hanger over the door handle on the outside of your bedroom door.

Adult guidance is needed for this activity.

Cut out along the dotted lines

COME IN!

I'M READY TO ROAR!

Cut out along
the dotted lines

KEEP OUT!

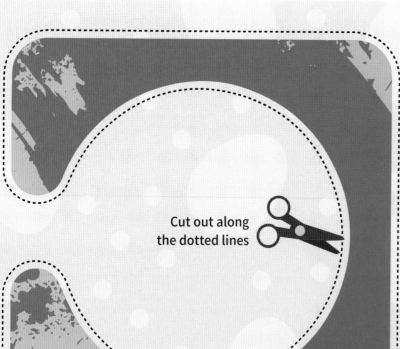

DINOSAUR DOZING!

FACT FINDER

Which dinosaur had a tiny brain the size of a chicken's egg? Follow the trails to discover the answer.

UTAHRAPTOR

MAIASAURA

It was me!

GASTONIA

Not me!

Try again!

QUESTION TIME

How much do you know about dinosaurs? Find out with this roar-some quiz!

All of the answers can be found somewhere in this book.

1
Which dinosaur had the strongest bite ever?

Pachycephalosaurus ☐

Tyrannosaurus ☐

2
What was Velociraptor the size of?

A wolf ☐

A hippo ☐

3
What did Ankylosaurus use its tail club for?

Attacking ☐

Swimming ☐

4
What caused dinosaurs to become extinct?

A volcano ☐

An asteroid ☐

5
Which dinosaur ran on tiptoes for speed?
Compsognathus ☐
Stegosaurus ☐

6
What did Diplodocus swallow to help digest its food?
Shells ☐
Stones ☐

7
What does Triceratops mean?
Four-legged animal ☐
Three-horned face ☐

8
What was Stegosaurus's brain the same size as?
A plum ☐
A football ☐

9
Which dinosaur ate fish?
Spinosaurus ☐
Argentinosaurus ☐

10
What did all dinosaurs have?
A tail ☐
Teeth ☐

Answers on pages 76-77

ANSWERS

PAGES 6-7
MAKE A MATCH

A and D, B and F, C and E.
G doesn't have a match.

PAGES 8-9
CAVE DASH

PAGES 10-15
PROFILES: PREDATORS

Food Fact – TOP.

True or False? – False, velociraptor was covered in feathers.

Up Close – C.

Egg Count – 8.

PAGE 16
DINO WORDS

PAGES 18-19
ON THE RUN

PAGES 26-27
DINO MATCH

PAGES 28-33
PROFILES: ONES WITH WEAPONS

Shadow Fun – C.

Stomping Stegosaurus – 10 footprints.

Question Time – Attacking.

Different Dino – C.

PAGE 38
WHO IS IT?

Spinosaurus.

PAGE 39
WORD HUNT

PAGES 42-43
PREHISTORIC PUZZLE

1. 5 bones.

3. 6 footprints.

4. C is the biggest.

6. There are more blue eggs.

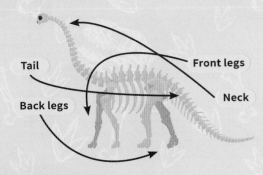

PAGES 46-51
PROFILES: GIANTS

Dino Bones:

Tail

Front legs

Back legs

Neck

Super Sail – C.

How Big? – An Argentinosaurus egg was the size of a football.

PAGE 52
CODE CRACKER

1. Teeth. 2. Fish. 3. Jaws.

PAGE 53
DOTTY DINO

Super Sequence - Red.

PAGES 56-57
STOMPING FEET

Count it! - 8 footprints.

PAGE 58
MEGA MIX-UP

Allosaurus – 3.

Diplodocus – 4.

Stegosaurus – 4.

PAGES 62
WHICH IS WRONG?

1 – C.   3 – E.

2 – B.   4 – D.

PAGES 64-69
PROFILES: LITTLE ONES

Egg hunt

Tiny Dino – A.

PAGES 73
FACT FINDER

Gastonia.

PAGES 74-75
QUESTION TIME

1. Tyrannosaurus.

2. A wolf.

3. Attacking.

4. An asteroid.

5. Compsognathus.

6. Stones.

7. Three-horned face.

8. A plum.

9. Spinosaurus.

10. A tail.